Reclaiming Home

A Journal for Clearing Clutter and Enjoying Your Home (Again)

Edited by Elizabeth B. Hill, MSW

Written by Elizabeth B. Hill, MSW with
Lianne Dixon, Mara Dowler, Donna V. Finocchiaro, Aina Hoskins, Rosemary King and Rachel Schemmerling

GREEN HEART LIVING PRESS

Reclaiming Home: A Journal for Clearing Clutter and Enjoying Your Home

ISBN (paperback): 978-1-954493-20-9

DEDICATION

for you, dear one,
may writing set you free

Table of Contents

How To Use This Book

There are many ways to use this journal. No way is wrong. Here are some ideas.

- **Create a morning or evening writing routine** - Build a writing routine with the questions in this journal serving as a springboard for a daily journaling practice.

- **Be random** - Flip through the pages and pick any page that catches your eyes to respond to.

- **Create a 12-day writing adventure** - For twelve days, set aside time each day to respond to one of the twelve sections of the book.

- **Reading and reflection experience** - Read the corresponding chapter in *Embrace Your Space*, then follow up with the questions in this journal by the same author.

- **Allow this to be part of a meditation or prayer practice** - Before beginning or after completing writing, allow space for meditation or prayer. Honoring and reclaiming home is sacred work.

- **Create a discussion group** - Use the questions in this journal to invoke discussion, reflection, and loving support for you and your friends.

- **Read it all at once.** Sit down and read the whole thing. Why not? Let it's ideas settle into the body. You can let it inform how you care for your home going forward. And you can decide which parts you'd like to dive deeper into.

Seeking Safety

1. Creating a Sanctuary
Aina Hoskins

I will take you through a process of how you can create a sanctuary in your space.

I invite you to start at your front door, take three deep breaths, set the intention of creating a sanctuary, and focus on what you want to feel in your space.

Now you can start a slow walk through your space. Do this in a clockwise manner.

As you walk, ask yourself:

"Do I love this?"

"What do I feel about every item I see and the colors?"

"Am I feeling expansive or congested?".

Now that you are noticing the energy and what you are feeling, it's time to release anything that is broken or not working, declutter where needed, release anything that you don't love.

Make a list of anything that needs to be removed or moved to a different space. Make a list of everything that needs to be fixed.

Sanctuary

To Be Removed

To Be Moved to Another Location

To Be Fixed

You may feel overwhelmed at this list right now – don't worry, it doesn't have to happen right away. Put aside 15 minutes a day to work on your list. Make sure to go with what feels good to you as you create your sanctuary.

Sanctuary

When it feels right, take some time to clear the energy in your space by smudging or burning a white candle and walk through your space clockwise. (Make sure you have a window open so the energy can go outside.)

I recommend finishing with a flower blessing. Leave a window slightly open while you go and get some fresh, fragrant and colorful flowers that make you happy. As you bring them into your space, set an intention and put the flowers near your front door. After a day, move them into your living space and remember your intention every time you look at them.

This is a process I personally do once a quarter to welcome in each season. Enjoy the process and remember your intention is what moves the energy.

Sanctuary

"Feng shui is like acupuncture for your architecture. It aligns your energy and creates flow."
Aina Hoskins

Sanctuary

About Aina

Aina L. Hoskins was born in Oslo, Norway. She achieved her MBA in Finance and has over 30 years of experience in the corporate world working with mergers, acquisitions, and budgeting. Aina is also an administrator for a charitable trust.

Aina has studied with many world-renowned teachers and is certified as a Transformational Life Mastery Consultant and Coach, EFT, Reiki, Feng Shui, Kinesiology, and many different prosperity programs.

As well as being Executive Officer at Squadron Capital, Executive Managing Director for eWomenNetwork CT, Aina is a speaker, success coach, and finance and Feng Shui consultant. She is passionate about helping women regain their power, shine their light, create prosperity, and accelerate their results, so we can all create lasting success.

Find Aina at ainahoskins@gmail.com

Sanctuary

Sanctuary

Sanctuary

Sanctuary

2. Creating Safe Spaces
Elizabeth B. Hill, MSW

I received signs throughout the course of reclaiming my home in the matriarchal palace. Just before I finally hired a home organizer, I tripped over electric cords two times in a row, and hurt each ankle and got giant bruises on both ankles. Apparently I didn't listen after the first ankle. When we moved into my grandma's home, the ceiling collapsed in a room that had been the most egregious of the rooms. I took this to mean we had permission to clear the whole place out. Not all signs are as dramatic as mine were. I tend to think signs get as big as they need to for us to pay attention.

Sit and reflect for a few moments.

Have there been any signs to change your current home environment? If so, what were they? Describe them here.

Safe Spaces

You deserve to have a safe and clean home. Are there any things in your home environment that are not safe or sanitary? Is there something that causes you shame or is really unhealthy for you to be living in the environment? List these here. (This book is a safe space. No one needs to see this but you.)

Safe Spaces

Now, go through this list. How will you approach each of these items? It is important to get these taken care of for the health and safety of yourself and those in your home. Ask for help if you need to. Having these taken care of will feel a massive relief.

Safe Spaces

"I have learned to embrace the spaces within and without. And we're all breathing easier for it."

Elizabeth B. Hill, MSW

About Elizabeth

Elizabeth is the CEO and founder of Green Heart Living and Green Heart Living Press. She is the best-selling author of *Be the Beacon, Success in Any Season, The Great Pause: Blessings and Wisdom from COVID-19, Love Notes: Daily Wisdom for the Soul,* and *Green Your Heart, Green Your World: Avoid Burnout, Save the World and Love Your Life.*

Elizabeth coaches clients on mindful leadership and writing to heal, inspire, and grow their impact in the world. Trained as a social worker, yoga teacher, and ontological coach, she weaves creativity, spirituality, and mindfulness into her work with clients. With over 15 years of experience writing and leading collaborations in the nonprofit sphere, Elizabeth brings a uniquely engaging approach to collaborative book projects. Elizabeth lives in Connecticut with her family.

Find Elizabeth at www.greenheartliving.com

Safe Spaces

Safe Spaces

Safe Spaces

Safe Spaces

Clearing Clutter

3. Healed from Within
Rosemary King

How can you set the mood before leaning into removing clutter from your home? Some examples I shared in my chapter were:

- Meditating and going deep within to learn more about myself and my thoughts and feelings surrounding the things I was passively clutching.
- Opening windows.
- Smudging the room.
- Listening to music.
- Using other techniques to remove any negative energy from my living space before tackling the clutter.

Write about which of these practices appeals to you and why? What have you tried? What has worked? What hasn't worked?

Healed from Within

Go through your home and assess the problem areas, both major and minor. Don't worry if you don't capture everything, but rather make a list of all the places you can immediately tell need your attention.

Once you have the assessment down on paper, highlight two or three areas you can focus your attention on over the next seven days and really let them shine! Choose simple places like the bathroom or a hallway closet. If you get those places done before the seven days then move on to the next area and continue going down the list to complete those micro-win areas before trying to tackle something like a garage or basement.

The point of this assessment is to help you determine which areas will be easy wins and which ones will likely take longer, so you're not stressing over the hard stuff first. Go one space at a time and finish it before moving on. Don't leave a space unfinished before starting to declutter a new area. When you finish an area, it'll give you a boost of energy and motivate you to tackle the harder hit areas in your home.

Problem Areas (Major)

Problem Areas (Minor)

Healed from Within

List two or three areas you'd like to focus your attention on in the next 7 days:

-

-

-

If you feel stuck at any point, remember, one bag at a time. Sometimes all you can achieve is one bag at a time. Whether that is a bag of trash, or a bag of clothes off the floor to be washed, or even a bag of things to donate, commit to removing one bag per day. Over time, you'll see that you are making progress, even if it feels slow.

"Removing clutter is not a race, it's a marathon. No one can run a marathon without training and we cannot remove all the clutter in one singular act."

Rosemary King

About Rosemary

Rosemary King is the owner of Heart-Led Concierge, a personal assistant service provider in Northeastern Connecticut. She offers home management, personal care management, decluttering and organizing, and other services to support families and small businesses. Heart-Led Concierge was created out of the need to spread love and compassion to moms with chronic illnesses. In 2009, Rosemary was diagnosed with a rare immune deficiency. As a result of her condition, she recognizes the challenges families like hers face when they're too sick to meet those needs. She is married to Wayne and they have six children, ages 12-21 years. Her family enjoys hiking, camping, and antiquing together. They also have a German Shepherd and pet ferret. Rosemary has been featured on popular sites such as Thrive Global, Medium, The Mighty, Realtor.com, and others. Fun fact, she was a makeover participant on the hit TV show, *What Not to Wear.* Her episode *Homecoming* is streaming on TLC.

Find Rosemary at www.heartledconcierge.com

Healed from Within

Healed from Within

Healed from Within

4. Letting Go - Our Relationship with Stuff
Rachel Schemmerling

Can you easily let go of things that friends and family gave to you? Do sentimental items hold you hostage? Find five objects in your home to donate today.

1)

2)

3)

4)

5)

Letting Go

Have you felt bad energy around things that you purchased from other people or have been given? Journal about how the item makes you feel, and then remove it from your home. Journal how you feel before and after it is gone.

Before

After

Letting Go

Would you be able to easily walk away from all your belongings? If you had to leave it all behind, what are three things that you cherish that you would take with you?

1)

2)

3)

Letting Go

"By taking the time to understand your relationship with your belongings and letting go of items that no longer serve you will change your life."
Rachel Schemmerling

About Rachel

Rachel Schemmerling is a Holistic Home Interior Design Consultant in Connecticut. Rachel's love for design began at an early age—both by nature and by nurture. She grew up in a 275-year-old Colonial farmhouse in coastal Connecticut which gave her a first look into the world of home design that was to become her passion. She now works with busy families to design an eco-friendly, serene, and healthy home that allows for functionality, sense of place, and peace of mind.

Find Rachel at www.timelesslivingdesigns.com

Letting Go

Letting Go

Letting Go

Letting Go

Release

5. What Else Needs to Go?
Lianne Dixon

The emotions we experience as we work through decluttering, cleaning, and organizing our "stuff" are good practice for when Spirit calls us to go a step further or walk into the fire. Decisions to declutter and release can be challenging, and they remind us that when we choose to engage the process actively, there's always a satisfying reward on the other side of the struggle. In addition, the experience reveals to us more who we are on a deeper level, how we want to show up, and how we can move past perceived limitations.

Perhaps, like me, you believe Spirit frequently invites us to go beyond the material and courageously enter into a conversation that asks, *"What do I need to release to become a more authentic version of who I am?"*

This section offers an opportunity to lean into the expansion of possibility when we ask Spirit what needs to be released from our lives. The following prompts are suggestions to start your path of discovery.

I ask these questions all the time - and the truth is I just as easily avoid them when I'm deep in the mud, unsure of my next move, and nearly paralyzed with fear. I hope you'll join me in wrapping this moment in grace and compassion because if what you know you need to release feels gigantic, you might glaze over this section. And that's okay. I trust you'll find it again when the time is right for you.

What Else Needs to Go?

What situation is triggering me?

When I think about this situation, what feelings come up? (Am I sad, angry, anxious, guilty, ashamed, afraid, overwhelmed, bitter, jealous?)

What Else Needs to Go?

What decision am I avoiding?

When I think about this, what feelings come up? (Am I sad, angry, anxious, guilty, ashamed, afraid, overwhelmed, bitter, jealous?)

What Else Needs to Go?

Which challenge have I been wanting to lean into but putting off?

When I think about this, what feelings come up? (Am I sad, angry, guilty, anxious, ashamed, afraid, overwhelmed, bitter, jealous?)

What Else Needs to Go?

Am I willing to take just one of these situations into conversation with Spirit? (I call this the beginning of a conversation because after we ask the question, we lean in to listen. We pay close attention to the messages we receive and we begin to note changes in our reactions and choices. Then, we give Spirit feedback, and Spirit responds again.)

Which situations will I focus on first? Why are these situations important to me?

What Else Needs to Go?

Now, create a request to Spirit:

Example: I am choosing to focus on "X" situation, which brings up a lot of self-loathing. **Request:** Spirit, show me who I am without self-loathing.

Example: I am choosing to focus on decision "Y" which brings up guilt for me. **Request:** Spirit, show me who I am without guilt.

I am choosing to focus on:

My request to Spirit:

Spirit, show me who I am without _____

_____

The task is to make the request daily, and any time the feeling comes up for us, then track it to see what happens over time.

Remember that nothing in life is static or moves in a straight line. This isn't about mastery. It's about discovery, so cut yourself some slack and go with the flow to see what else is possible for you. The call to release more of what no longer serves us will continue far beyond this moment, sometimes stretching us in the most uncomfortable of ways. And that's okay. We may not like or appreciate it at the moment, but what if this is the work we are created for? And maybe, *just maybe*, what if we believed that Spirit really does have our backs?

What Else Needs to Go?

What Else Needs to Go?

"Spirit, show me who I am when I don't have any doubt about whether or not you've got my back. And so it is."

Lianne Dixon

About Lianne

Lianne Dixon is a certified family coach with a Bachelor's in Social Work. Her mission is to guide and support parents who are tired of the clash, conflict, and disrespectful attitudes that frequently accompany adolescence. Releasing patterns that no longer serve their families, she introduces parents to high-impact strategies that immediately begin to build respect, trust, and strengthen communication between them and their teen, to finally end the struggle and create a more peaceful home.

Find Lianne at www.gettingrealcoach.com

What Else Needs to Go?

What Else Needs to Go?

What Else Needs to Go?

What Else Needs to Go?

Receive

6. *From Chaos to Calm*
Mara Dowler

One of the simplest ways to elevate our mood is to practice gratitude. Acknowledging the goodness in our lives and in the world has a positive impact on our happiness and whole being: mind, body, and spirit. Saying thank you is a simple yet powerful act.

Take a few moments to think about someone you would like to thank for their kindness. Write them a letter expressing your gratitude. Send it or keep it in your journal. It could be someone currently in your life or someone who is no longer in your life. It could be yourself.

Calm

Awareness is the first step toward making a change. What change do you want to make in your life? Perhaps you wish to make a change in your physical space in your home. You could begin by becoming more aware of your belongings. Do you feel like you have too much? Enough? Do you want more? Can you distinguish between what is important or special?

Spend some time thinking about how you want your home to look, feel, and function. How is your amount of "stuff" related to your vision? Write down what change you want to make and then what your ideal lifestyle looks like. Be as detailed and as descriptive as you can be.

Calm

Do you tend to see the glass half full or half empty? It doesn't matter, really. But can you shift your mindset to see the other perspective? We can begin to shift our perspective from negative to positive when we reframe it. It takes practice, but it becomes quite empowering when we are able to improve our attitude, open our mind, and give ourselves - and others - grace. For example, when it comes to clearing clutter, instead of focusing on "what can I get rid of?" try to shift your focus to "what do I choose to keep?" In other words, what serves a purpose or speaks to your heart? What do you use, need, or love?

How can you begin to shift your perspective and choose joy? Write down some recurring negative thoughts you have and then reframe them in a positive light and write down the new perspective.

Calm

"With awareness, intention, patience, and commitment, you can transform your outer world and your inner world from chaos to calm."

Mara Dowler

Calm

About Mara

Mara Dowler is a Professional Home Organizer and Certified KonMari Consultant who has personally experienced surprising, positive, life-changing effects through Enneagram wisdom, Mind Body Spirit work, and the KonMari Method™ of decluttering and organizing. Mara created Bluebird Home Organizing, LLC in 2019 in hopes of inspiring others to discover their own life-changing magic. She believes that with the proper tools and guidance, anyone can get and stay organized. Often, the result is so much more than a tidy home; it's a personal transformation from a chaotic lifestyle to a calmer one. Mara happily serves clients along the Connecticut Shoreline, where she lives with her husband and their four sons.

Find Mara at www.bluebirdhome.net

Calm

Calm

Calm

7. Making Room to Receive
Elizabeth B. Hill, MSW

Consider your current housing situation. Reflect on the cost in terms of time and money that you spend keeping it in this state.

For instance, your closet may be disorganized. This may cause you to have difficulty selecting an outfit in the morning, which in turn may cost you in terms of energy, time (being late to work or getting started late on a project). Get detailed...if you are losing half an hour choosing an outfit and this happens every morning, how much is that hour costing you?

Receive

If you didn't have to spend this time, what could this make possible? Reflect on time, money, opportunities, health, well-being, and quality of life?

Receive

Who will you ask for support in caring for your home?

Receive

"By releasing the stress and weight of objects and burdens, my mind is free to be openly creative, to focus on my work, enjoy time with family, and be open to receive."
Elizabeth B. Hill, MSW

Receive

Receive

Receive

Receive

8. Offering Peace of Mind
Donna Finocchario

Going through a housing transition and moving can feel overwhelming. Here are some questions that will help you on this path.

What am I going to do with all my stuff?

Peace of Mind

What should I take to my new home?

What are my items worth? What is my plan for these items?

Peace of Mind

"I had found my passion, my driving force in life, and the bonus was I was helping others change their lives for the better, too."

Donna Finocchiaro

About Donna

Donna Finocchiaro is an entrepreneur and businesswoman who is general manager for her home-grown professional organizing company, Lotus Transitions, LLC. Over the years, Donna has helped more than one thousand people through hands-on help, mentoring, or professional speaking. The company has a specialty niche in supporting the senior citizen marketplace with downsizing, and also handles home organization, staging and selling unwanted items. Donna was honored to be an active member of two Extreme Makeover: Home Edition CT builds and spearheads a team that supports hundreds of inner-city school-aged children each year.

Find Donna at www.LotusTransitions.us

Peace of Mind

Peace of Mind

Peace of Mind

9. Your Home Thanks You

As we are reclaiming our homes, it is very important that we give ourselves credit for our accomplishments. Use the following pages to keep a record of all the ways you have shown love to your home.

Your Home Thanks You

Your Home Thanks You

Your Home Thanks You

10. Celebration

Many of us get so caught up in the mountain of things that need doing that once we accomplish a task, we just head on over to the next thing on the to-do list. You deserve to celebrate and be celebrated! I've found that celebrating in small ways keeps the momentum going so that over time you will be amazed by the results. How you want to celebrate is up to you. Sometimes celebration for me is going out to dinner with a friend. Sometimes it's bringing a favorite food in. And I often want to celebrate by having some time alone to do anything I want! Which can be nothing! Celebrations don't need to be a big party or to cost money. Celebrations can be small pockets of time getting to experience things that you enjoy.

What tasks are on your to-do list? How will you celebrate these when they are achieved?

Celebration

How did you celebrate? Each time you celebrate a win in reclaiming your home, write it here.

Celebration

Celebration

Celebration

About Green Heart Living

Green Heart Living's mission is to make the world a more loving and peaceful place, one person at a time. Green Heart Living Press publishes inspirational books and stories of transformation, making the world a more loving and peaceful place, one book at a time.

Whether you have an idea for an inspirational book and want support through the writing process - or your book is already written and you are looking for a publishing path - Green Heart Living can help you get your book out into the world.

You can meet Green Heart authors on the Green Heart Living YouTube channel and the Green Heart Living podcast.

www.greenheartliving.com

Made in the USA
Middletown, DE
17 February 2022

61144528R00053